Barry Gifford's

PERDITA DURANGO

Script Adaptation:
BOB CALLAHAN

Art:
SCOTT GILLIS

AVON BOOKS ◆ NEW YORK

Neon Lit: Barry Gifford's Perdita Durango is an original publication of Avon Books. This work has never appeared in graphic form. Any similarity to actual persons or events is purely coincidental.

AVON BOOKS
A division of
The Hearst Corporation
1350 Avenue of the Americas
New York, New York 10019

Copyright © 1995 by Bob Callahan Studios
Film stills courtesy of the film producers and The San Francisco Academy of the Narrative Arts
Published by arrangement with Bob Callahan Studios
Library of Congress Catalog Card Number: 95-94315
ISBN: 0-380-77109-8

Neon Lit Editor: Bob Callahan
Neon Lit Design: Art Spiegelman
Neon Lit Avon Books Senior Editor: Rachel Klayman
Neon Lit Production: Andi Plantenberg, Anne Marie Spagnuolo,
    Diane Godzinski, Eileen O Malley Callahan. Map of Ireland: Leslie Jackson.

First Avon Books Printing: December 1995

AVON TRADEMARK REG. U.S. PAT. OFF. AND IN OTHER COUNTRIES, MARCA REGISTRADA, HECHO EN U.S.A.

Printed in the USA

QPM 10 9 8 7 6 5 4 3 2 1

WHEN AZTECS KISS

One of Barry Gifford's enduring strengths as a writer is his prodigious ability to create a near assembly line of real knucklehead characters. This is strange, actually. Like his fellow scriptwriter, Quentin Tarantino, Barry seems to have a breeding ground for sweet but violent oddballs somewhere in the back of his head.

Barry Gifford's *Perdita Durango* was chosen as the second volume in the Neon Lit series largely because of its tarot card approach to the chaos and violence of contemporary America. Our treatment owes a great deal not just to Barry, but also to David Lynch. This book was in fact created after the experience of viewing many, many times the Lynch/Gifford collaboration on the movie version of *Wild At Heart*.

Uniquely, perhaps, we imagine our own Perdita as Ms. Aztec Sacrifice 1995. As you still can hear it being said this very evening in low-life saloons all along the Rio Grande, this is the kind of woman who would actually bite out your heart. Yes, she would.

For our Perdita Durango, particularly at the grave of her dead sister Juana, this is mostly a question of history.

Mention should be made, certainly, of the nature of Scott Gillis's art. The medium — many will realize — is scratchboard. As Mr. Gillis etches, he lets in the light. This is the kind of work that was undoubtedly begun by Hibernian monks and angels a thousand years ago. These days, some would perhaps claim it impossible to create a book as complex and detailed as our scratchboard Perdita, but evidence to the contrary, dear reader, is now in your hand.

As for the language of this unique telling of the story, while Mr. Gillis and I set many new scenes — and created many new environments only hinted at in the original text — we were both delighted nonetheless when, in the final weeks of production, Barry Gifford himself volunteered to go over every line of dialogue in this book, allowing the characters he had originally invented to speak as he uniquely heard them speaking, into the strangeness of the new situations and circumstances Mr. Gillis and I had created for them. There was a lovely, looping feeling to this gesture, as if the project had found its own appropriate and natural end.

And so off we go now with Aztec Girl and her small-time Cali Cartel pal, on the road from N'awlins to LALA Land. Working with Barry, Scott and Art has been a thrill. It is also great how, in the end, at Avon, this project ended up in the able and supportive hands of Rachel Klayman. I hope that the collective excitement we have all felt creating our own bonita Perdita works its way into the pleasures you feel while engaged with this book.

—Bob Callahan

PERDITA MET MANNY IN THE LOUNGE
OF THE SAN ANTONIO AIRPORT. HE WAS FAT BUT NEAT.
HE WIPED HIS THIN LIPS WITH A NAPKIN.

AFTER FORKING DOWN HIS LAST BITE, MANNY SAT DOWN AT PERDITA'S TABLE.

SWEETHEART, BRING ME A BUD, AND GIVE THIS GIRL ANYTHING SHE WANTS.

3

DEPARTING FLIGHTS

FLIGHTS	GATE	DESTINATION	DEPARTURE	STATUS
607	07	DALLAS-CHICAGO	05:30	ON TIME
087	12	ST LOUIS	06:00	ON TIME
904	16	NEW ORLEANS	06:30	CANCELLED
032	04	MEXICO CITY	07:30	ON TIME
610	10	PHOENIX-LA	07:30	ON TIME
055	14	DALLAS-FT WORTH	08:00	ON TIME

YOU HEADIN' SOMEWHERE?

NOT ANYMORE. YOURSELF?

PHOENIX. FOUR DAY COMPUTER CONVENTION. I'M A SALESMAN.

AS MANNY DRONED ON, PERDITA LISTENED IN ON THE CONVERSATION AT THE NEXT TABLE.

WHY DOES YOUR MOM GO OUT WITH HIM?

I DON'T KNOW. MAYBE HE'S HUNG LIKE A CROCODILE.

DO YOU AND YOUR MOM EVER TALK ABOUT SEX?

GET REAL. SHE'D DROP DEAD IF SHE KNEW HALF OF WHAT I'VE DONE.

PERDITA WATCHED THE TWO GIRLS WALK AWAY.
SHE FELT A SUDDEN DESIRE TO STAB THEM BOTH
IN THE THROAT, IN THE CHEST. SHE IMAGINED THE SIGHT
OF DARK BLOOD RUNNING DOWN THEIR TRIM AND
WELL-TONED TENNIS PLAYER LEGS. JUST AS SUDDENLY,
THE IMPULSE PASSED.

MY NAME'S
MANNY FLYNN,
HALF JEW, HALF MICK.

MINE'S
PERDITA DURANGO,
HALF TEX, HALF MEX.

7

AS HE KEPT ON TALKING, A FATHER AND TWO YOUNG TWIN GIRLS SAT DOWN AT A NEARBY TABLE.

THE GIRLS MADE PERDITA SAD. THEY REMINDED HER OF HER OWN TWIN SISTER.

JUANA HAD BEEN SHOT BY HER DRUNKEN HUSBAND, TONY. TONY THEN KILLED THE GIRLS BEFORE BLOWING OFF THE TOP OF HIS OWN SKULL.

PERDITA MISSED JUANA. SHE GUESSED SHE MIGHT FOREVER. TONY SHE COULD ALWAYS HAVE LIVED WITHOUT.

8

PERDITA NOW GREW WEARY LISTENING TO MANNY.
SHE LOOKED HIM STRAIGHT IN THE EYE AND SAID,

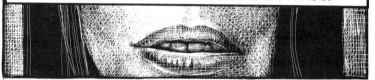

"YOU WANT ME TO COME TO PHOENIX WITH YOU?
YOU PAY MY WAY, BUY MY MEALS, GET ME BACK.
I'LL KEEP YOUR DICK HARD FOR FOUR DAYS.
AT THE CONVENTION I'LL DO SOME BUSINESS TOO."

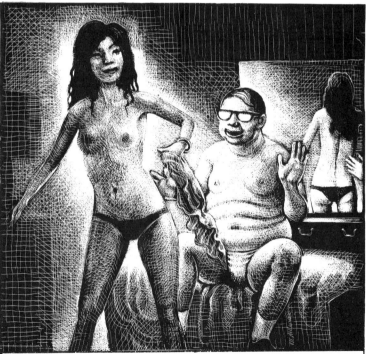

"PLENTY OF GUYS AT YOUR HOTEL, RIGHT?
FIFTY DOLLARS FOR SHOWING TIT AND MILKING THE COW.
ALL OF IT QUICK AND CLEAN."

9

THE GOOD LIFE

PERDITA DURANGO MET ROMEO DOLOROSA
IN SAINT LOUIS CEMETERY IN THE CITY OF NEW ORLEANS.

11

ROMEO ARRIVED IN NEW ORLEANS FROM THE ISLANDS.	PERDITA HAD BEEN IN TOWN JUST A COUPLE OF DAYS.

ROMEO HAD COME TO TOWN FOR BANKING BUSINESS.

WANTED FOR MURDER
ROMEO DOLOROSA
AKA
SHAKEEM NABOOTIE
AKA
THE COBRA MAN
NARCOTICS TRAFFICKING

DOLOROSA   DOLOROSA   DOLOROSA

BANK OF JAMAICA   JAMAICA POLICE

PERDITA THOUGHT HE HAD AN UNUSUAL SMILE.

IT WAS GOOD TO BE BACK IN NEW ORLEANS.

ROMEO'S COUSIN REGGIE WORKED THERE FOR THE LOCAL MAFIA GODFATHER.

IN THIS VERY STRANGE CITY REGINALD SAN PEDRO SULA HAD BECOME AN IMPORTANT MAN TO KNOW.

AS REGGIE'S GUESTS, PERDITA AND ROMEO SPENT THEIR FIRST NIGHT IN ONE OF THE MOB'S LUXURY HOTELS.

ROMEO WAS FALLING IN LOVE WITH PERDITA. HE FELT COMPELLED TO TELL HER WHY HE HAD GONE ON THE RUN.

"BACK IN THE ISLANDS, PEOPLE FEARED ME."

"THEY BELIEVED I WAS A BADASS VOODOO PRIEST."

14

"THIS WAS GREAT FOR BUSINESS, OF COURSE. EACH DAY WE WOULD GREET THE PLANES FROM CALI. EACH NIGHT WE WOULD SEND BOATS TO MIAMI BEACH. NOW, I DO NOT KNOW WHAT TO DO."

WELL, HOMBRE, YOU MUST SEND THEM A SIGNAL.

YES, BUT WHAT? WHAT?

FEED ME FIRST. THEN WE CAN TALK.

WHAT WE WILL DO IS KILL SOMEBODY. THEN WE EAT THEM.

THAT SHOULD SEND THEM A SIGNAL.

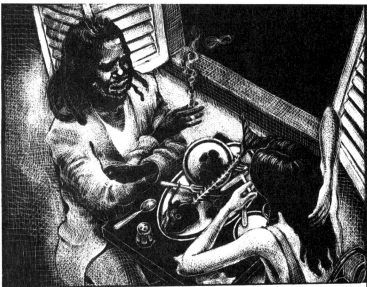

ROMEO GRITTED HIS TEETH. "BELIEVE IT," HE TOLD HIMSELF. "LIFE WITH THIS WOMAN WILL BE WITHOUT APOLOGIES."

SEX AMONG THE AZTECS

TEXAS 300 MILES

PERDITA AND ROMEO LEFT NEW ORLEANS
THE NEXT MORNING FOR REGGIE'S PLACE
ON THE GULF DOWN IN TEXAS.

18

19

BACK IN NEW ORLEANS, REGGIE WAS CALLED
TO A SPECIAL MEETING OF THE SANTOS ORGANIZATION.
NEW FACES HAD BEGUN TO SHOW UP IN NEW ORLEANS.
CHANGE HAD NOW BECOME THE RULE OF THE DAY.

THE MEETING WAS HELD AT SANTOS' HEADQUARTERS
ON CAMP STREET.

SANTOS' NEPHEW, POPPY PAPAVERO, CHAIRED THE MEETING. POPPY WAS A RECENT GRADUATE OF THE BUSINESS SCHOOL AT L.S.U.

"GENTLEMEN, THANKS IN GREAT PART TO OUR VISITORS HERE, WE ARE NOW ON THE THRESHOLD OF AN AGE OF BOLD NEW OPPORTUNITIES."

"DUE TO BULK ORDERS AND BULK SHIPMENTS, WE WILL NOW BE ABLE TO OFFER OUR PREFERRED CUSTOMERS A FINER GRADE OF PRODUCT AT MUCH BETTER QUANTITY DISCOUNTS."

"OUR FRIENDS HERE WILL SUPPLY THE PROPER LAUNDRY SERVICES WHEN THE PRODUCT REACHES ADDIS ABABA."

"THE PRODUCT WILL BE BROUGHT DOWN FROM OUR ALLIES' FIELDS IN THE MOUNTAINS OF AFGHANISTAN."

"SYRIAN TANKERS WILL BRING THE PRODUCT WITH U.S. NAVAL ESCORT THROUGH THE STRAITS OF HARMUZ. AS ALWAYS, I'M SURE WE CAN COUNT ON THE NAVY'S AID."

"AFTER THE PRODUCT ARRIVES IN GALVESTON, WE WILL USE OUR REFRIGERATED TRUCKS TO MOVE IT ACROSS THE STATES."

IT'S A NEW DAY, GENTLEMEN, FILLED WITH THE PROMISE OF BOLD NEW OPPORTUNITIES.

REGGIE THOUGHT OF HIS COUSIN ROMEO.

"BUSINESS IS BOOMING," REGGIE THOUGHT. "THERE MAY BE WORK FOR ROMEO AFTER ALL."

24

The town of Rayne is the capital of the Louisiana Frog Industry

Last year more than 500,000 frogs were shipped from Rayne to supply houses aquariums and universities around the world.

On a warm summer day as many as 10,000 new frogs might be captured & brought in dragging & kicking from the neighboring swamps.

ACROSS THE TEXAS BORDER LINE

WITH DUANE AND ESTELLE BOUND AND TIED
IN THE BACKSEAT, THE CHEVROLET BARRELLED DOWN U.S. 10
PAST LAKE CHARLES ON ITS WAY
ACROSS THE TEXAS BORDER LINE.

27

WHERE ARE YOU TAKING US?

RELAX, HOMBRE. WE'RE JUST GOING FOR A LITTLE RIDE.

HER NAME'S PERDITA. MINE'S ROMEO. WHAT SHOULD WE CALL THE TWO OF YOU? IT LOOKS LIKE WE'RE ALL GOING TO BE FRIENDS FOR A LITTLE WHILE.

29

SHERIFF RIP FORD WAS IN BED WITH A PROSTITUTE WHEN HE FIRST GOT THE CALL.

WHAT'S UP, FED?

TYRONE "RIP" FORD WAS SHERIFF OF LARRY LEE COUNTY IN EAST TEXAS. THE FORDS HAD BEEN SHERIFFS OF LARRY LEE FOR AS LONG AS ANYONE COULD REMEMBER.

NO, I'M FINE. WHY'D YOU CALL, FED?

AT THE BATTLE OF SABINE PASS TWO OF RIP'S UNCLES WERE KILLED TRYING TO PROTECT LARRY LEE FROM AN INVASION OF A RENEGADE BRIGADE OF BLACK SOLDIERS.

AFTER THE BATTLE THE SURVIVING SOLDIERS WERE HANGED FROM THE COURTHOUSE STEPS IN DOWNTOWN LEESVILLE.

THE HANGING WAS 120 YEARS AGO.

120 YEARS, AND NO BLACK MAN HAD TAKEN UP RESIDENCE IN GOOD OLD LARRY LEE COUNTY YET.

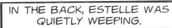

IN THE BACK, ESTELLE WAS QUIETLY WEEPING.

IT REALLY HAD BEEN A TERRIBLE YEAR.

HER FIRST COLLEGE SEMESTER HAD BEEN REAL DISAPPOINTING.

MEETING DUANE HAD BEEN THE ONLY GOOD THING TO HAPPEN.

ESTELLE THOUGHT OF HER MOM, GLORY ANN SATISFY.

MOM WAS A SMALL TOWN MINISTER'S DAUGHTER.

GLORY ANN LOVED SMALL TOWNS. SHE NEVER DID FEEL COMFORTABLE IN DALLAS. SHE COULDN'T GET USED TO NOT SEEING THE SAME PEOPLE DAY AFTER DAY.

ESTELLE THOUGHT OF
HER DAD, E.T. SATISFY.

E.T. WASN'T CALLED E.T.
BECAUSE OF THE MOVIE.

HIS DADDY HAD
NICKNAMED
HIM E.T. AS A BABY.

GRANDDADDY WAS
A BIG, BIG FAN
OF MISTER ERNEST TUBB.

E.T. DROVE A 7-UP TRUCK AND SMOKED THREE ARK CIGARETTES EVERY DAY.

ACTUALLY HE ONLY PUFFED ON TWO OF THEM...

AND KEPT THE THIRD ON HAND TO SHOW THE MOOCHERS JUST HOW TERRIBLE THE DAMN THINGS TASTED.

35

ESTELLE NOW LOOKED AT BOTH PERDITA AND ROMEO. THEN SHE BEGAN TO CRY. DUANE WAS CRYING TOO.

"OH GOD," DUANE THOUGHT. "THIS LIFE'S SURE GOT QUESTION MARKS SCATTERED AROUND LIKE DOGSHIT IN AN EMPTY LOT. I GUESS I AIN'T BEEN STEPPIN' CAREFUL ENOUGH."

BAD MOON RISING

RANCHO
NEGRITA
INFANTE

A HUNDRED AND FIFTY MILES INTO TEXAS,
THEY FINALLY REACHED REGGIE'S RANCH.

38

39

THAT EVENING, REGGIE ARRIVED FROM NEW ORLEANS.

"YOU'RE IN," REGGIE TOLD HIS COUSIN.
"TWENTY GRAND FOR DRIVING ONE TRUCK TO LOS ANGELES.
JUST DON'T ASK WHAT YOU'RE CARRYING."

"MR. SANTOS HAS MADE ARRANGEMENTS
WITH JIMMY'S PEOPLE AND J. EDNA."

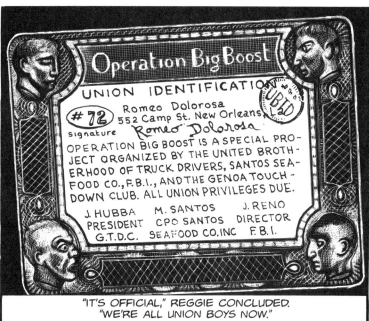

"IT'S OFFICIAL," REGGIE CONCLUDED.
"WE'RE ALL UNION BOYS NOW."

LATER THAT NIGHT, AFTER REGGIE HAD GONE TO BED,
PERDITA GOT TO THINKING ABOUT DUANE AND ESTELLE.

WHICH ONE, HOMBRE?
THE GIRL OR THE BOY?

TOUGH, CHIQUITA.
HAVE YOU GONE SOFT
ON THIS BOY?

MAYBE, HOMBRE,
MAYBE. HOW ABOUT
SU VACA?

"MAYBE WE SHOULD KEEP THEM BOTH. FOR OUR PURPOSES IT IS GOOD TO HAVE A FEW YOUNG ANGLOS AROUND."

PERSONAL CHECK? SURE!

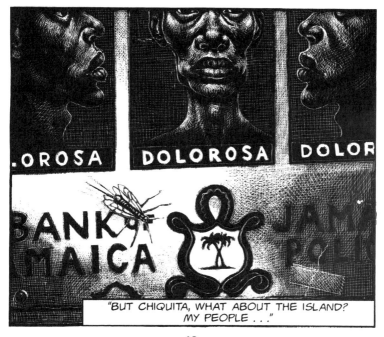

"BUT CHIQUITA, WHAT ABOUT THE ISLAND? MY PEOPLE . . ."

44

THAT OLD TIME RELIGION

THE CEREMONY BEGAN AT DUSK.

"WE ARE ON ONE SIDE OF THE GREAT RIVER,"
THE HIGH PRIEST INTONED.

"YOU MUST CROSS OVER. . ."

". . . INTO THE GREAT NIGHT."

46

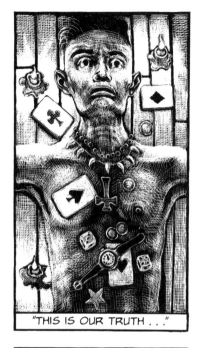

"THIS IS OUR TRUTH . . ."

"THE TRUTH THAT IS KNOWN."

"IT SHALL MAKE US STRONG."

"IT WILL BRING NEW LIFE."

"THIS IS OUR OFFERING . . ."

" . . . TO THE MUSIC OF NIGHT."

48

50

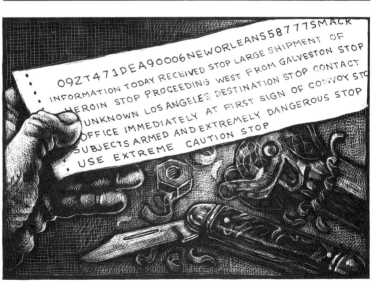

The morning after the sacrifice, Romeo and Perdita mounted up to leave for Los Angeles.

"NOT SO MUCH
. . . ANYMORE."

BACK AT THE SHERIFF'S OFFICE, RIP AND FED
WERE DISCUSSING THE TELEX.

"FED, IF THAT SHIPMENT IS ANYWHERE AROUND HERE, THEY'RE
GONNA HAVE TO HAUL IT THROUGH THE CROSSROADS."

" .. MAKE A FEW CALLS, FED".

"LET'S GET
EVERYBODY MOVIN'."

55

"FED, WHAT DO YOU KNOW ABOUT THIS BLACK MAGIC DRUG CULT OPERATIN' OUT OF THE OLD NEGRITA INFANTE?"

"NOT MUCH, SHERIFF. 'CEPT THE INDIANS SAY THE GUY RUNNIN' IT CAN CHANGE HIMSELF INTO A JAGUAR."

"RIGHT. A NAGUAL."

A WHAT?

56

"SOMEBODY WITH A JAGUAR'S HEAD AND A MAN'S BODY. INDIANS BELIEVE ONLY A REAL SANTERO CAN PULL OFF A STUNT LIKE THAT."

"WHOEVER THIS GUY IS, HE SURE GOT THE INDIANS AROUND HERE HALF-CRAZY."

57

58

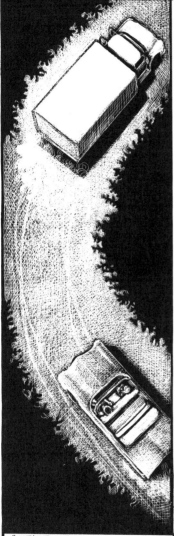

AS THE TWO WOMEN FOLLOWED BEHIND ROMEO IN THE CHEVY, ESTELLE BEGAN TO CRY AGAIN.

"WE'RE NEXT, AREN'T WE?," ESTELLE SOBBED. "YOU AND ROMEO ARE THE TWO MOST EVIL PEOPLE ON THIS EARTH."

THE TWO OF YOU ARE NOTHING BUT SOULLESS GHOULS.

"IF YOU COULD, I BET YOU'D RAPE A CORPSE."

PERDITA COULD SEE THE CROSSROADS UP AHEAD.
THEN SHE TURNED TO ESTELLE.
"GOD DON'T TAKE THOSE THINGS THAT SERIOUSLY, GRINGA.
KEEP ON TALKING. SEE HOW SERIOUS HE IS ABOUT YOU."

PETE ARMANDARIZ WAS ONE
OF MARCELLO SANTOS' FAVORITE SOLDIERS.

HE WAS ONCE ONE OF THE
BEST DRIVERS IN THE MOB.

... BEFORE HE STARTED
TAKING THOSE GODDAMN PILLS.

62

DAMN, CHIQUITA. WE GOTTA GET MOVING NOW!

WAY THIS BITCH KEEP TALKIN' SHE AIN'T GONNA LIVE TO SEE L.A.!

WITH TWO MILLION IN MOB HEROIN IN THE BACK OF THE TRUCK, ROMEO AND PERDITA WERE NOW HEADING WEST.

SMALL TOWN AFTER SMALL TOWN NOW FLEW BY AS THEY STUCK EAST TEXAS IN THEIR BACK POCKET.

YOU EVER SEE THAT MOVIE VERA CRUZ?

GARY COOPER, RIGHT?

. . . AND BURT LANCASTER. IT CHANGED MY LIFE.

SAINT BURT, MAN!

"... THAT BLACK OUTFIT, BLACK HAT, PEARL-HANDLED REVOLVER ..."

"... AND 108 GLEAMING WHITE FUCKING TEETH. SAINT BURT'S THE MAN."

ARE YOU GOING TO KILL US, MR. DOLOROSA?

DON'T KNOW YET, KID. THIS AIN'T NO MOVIE.

WOODY DUMAS WAS AT HIS DESK IN NEW ORLEANS WHEN THE CALL CAME IN FROM THE JUNCTION. IT WAS THE FBI ON THE PHONE.

YEAH, DOYLE, I HEAR YOU. OF COURSE IT'S SANTOS' WORK. MOB BUSINESS ALL THE WAY.

NO. YOU BET. IT'S STILL OUR CASE.

TIME THIS OLD BIRD DOG GOT BACK ON HUNT.

"THIS GUY WASN'T THERE TEN MINUTES BEFORE HE GOT HIS HEAD BLOWN OFF BY SOME DRIVE-BY GUY WITH A SHOTGUN."

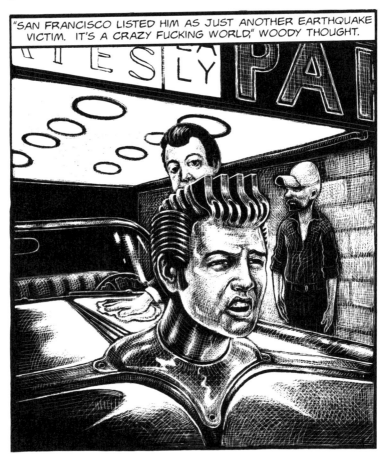

"SAN FRANCISCO LISTED HIM AS JUST ANOTHER EARTHQUAKE VICTIM. IT'S A CRAZY FUCKING WORLD," WOODY THOUGHT.

A FEW MILES OUT OF SAN ANTONIO, ROMEO SIGNALLED PERDITA TO PULL OVER TO THE SHOULDER OF THE ROAD.

THERE'S A DUDE I'D LIKE TO VISIT A FEW MILES FROM HERE. FOLLOW ME CLOSELY.

THE LA FLORIDA CLUB WAS OWNED BY
BIG CHIEF AMAURY CATALINA, WHO CLAIMED TO BE
A DIRECT DESCENDANT OF ANCIENT AZTEC KINGS.

ROMEO ONLY KNEW THAT THE BIG CHIEF HAD
A BIG NOSE PROBLEM. HE OWED ROMEO $10,000.

73

PERDITA STOPPED AT THE GRAVE SITE
OF HER SISTER JUANA ON THE WAY OUT OF TOWN.

TRUCK-O-RAMA

AT DAWN, THEY STOPPED NEAR THE NEW MEXICO BORDER.
ROMEO AND ESTELLE WENT DIRECTLY TO BREAKFAST;
PERDITA AND DUANE WENT WANDERING AROUND THE MUSEUM.

WE'RE HERE FOR A WHILE?

COUPLE OF HOURS, ANYWAY.

IT ALL BEGINS WITH DAISY

WHY? YOU AND MS. POISON FIGURE TO SKIP OUT ON US?

NO. NO WAY.

CHICKENS ARE OUR FRIENDS

HOT ON THE TRAIL OF *ROMEO* AND *PERDITA*, DEA AGENT WOODY DUMAS STOPPED FOR A DRINK AT SPARKY & BUDDY'S JUST EAST OF LAKE.

WOODY ENJOYED SPARKY & BUDDY'S PLACE. HE PARTICULARLY ENJOYED FLIRTING WITH SHERRY LOUISE, SPARKY & BUDDY'S BARTENDER. AT FIRST HE HARDLY NOTICED THE ANGRY LITTLE MAN AT THE END OF THE BAR.

WOODY WAS NOT THE ONLY ONE TRYING TO FIND *ROMEO* AND *PERDITA*. ON THE ROAD FOR THREE DAYS NOW WITHOUT ANY SLEEP, E.T. SATISFY WAS DETERMINED TO FIND HIS DAUGHTER OR ELSE.

SONS OF BITCHES AIN'T NEVER GONNA FIND HER.

BASTARDS GOT MY DAUGHTER PROBABLY OVER THE BORDER BY NOW.

COME AGAIN, PARDNER?

DAMN DRUG DEALERS GOT MY DAUGHTER. SONS OF BITCHES. CHINK COUNTERFEITERS MAKIN' ROLEXES, COMPUTER INNARDS, GOVERNMENT'LL GO AFTER IT LIKE COCKSTARVED BANSHEES. LET IT BE SOME POOR LITTLE TEXAS GAL GETS GRABBED OFF THE STREET AND THEY CAN'T FIGURE THEIR ASSHOLE WIPES NORTH OR SOUTH. ECONOMICS IS WHAT IT IS, PURE AND SMILIN' SIMPLE. THAT'S WHAT I SAY.

80

81

82

AFTER BREAKFAST THEY DROVE ALL DAY, DEEP INTO NEW MEXICO. BY DUSK, THEY WERE ON THE OUTSKIRTS OF WHITE SANDS, NEW MEXICO.

TELL YOU WHO MY HEROES ARE, DUANE. GUYS LIKE OLD JAMES ROBERTS WOULD HAVE TO BE ONE OF THEM.

ROBERTS JUST ROSE UP AND SHOT ELEVEN PEOPLE -- EIGHT OF 'EM WERE KIDS -- ONE EASTER SUNDAY A FEW YEARS AGO BACK IN OHIO.

WHITE SANDS WAS NAMED WHITE SANDS BECAUSE OF THE MASSIVE AMOUNTS OF GYPSUM IN THE SOIL. OVER MILLIONS OF YEARS, JUST ABOUT EVERYTHING -- THE MICE, THE LIZARDS, THE BIRDS, PLANTS -- TURNED WHITE TO BLEND INTO THIS VERY UNUSUAL ENVIRONMENT.

PEOPLE SAY THE MAD VISIONARY SPANISH MONK, CABEZA DE VACA, MAY HAVE BEEN THE FIRST EUROPEAN TO WANDER INTO THE WHITE SANDS BASIN AREA.

THEN THERE WAS THIS GUY, HOWARD UNRUH, BACK IN NEW JERSEY. HE TOOK OUT 13 PEOPLE IN 12 MINUTES.

WHEN THEY CAUGHT HIM, HE SAID "I COULD HAVE GOT 1000 IF I HAD ENOUGH GODDAMN BULLETS."

GERONIMO USED THE LOCAL HILLS AS HOME IN BETWEEN HIS RAIDING PARTIES. BILLY THE KID KILLED A COUPLE OF MEN HERE DURING A RANGE WAR.

NOW, WHEN IT COMES TO HEROES, I DON'T COUNT ARMIES AND I DON'T COUNT SERIAL KILLERS -- PEOPLE WHO PLAN TO KILL OVER A PERIOD OF TIME.

WHITE SANDS HAD BECOME A TOP SECRET MISSILE BASE BY THE END OF WORLD WAR II. THE U.S. GOVERNMENT EXPERIMENTED WITH ITS OWN V-2 PROGRAM ON THE SITE.

MY HEROES ARE ALL PEOPLE WHO JUST CAN'T TAKE IT ANYMORE. WITHOUT WARNING THEY JUST EXPLODE.

IT WAS AT WHITE SANDS, IN 1945, AT A SITE CALLED TRINITY, THAT THE U.S. EXPLODED THE WORLD'S FIRST ATOMIC BOMB. GROUND ZERO IS AS SILENT AS A CATHEDRAL MOST NIGHTS NOW.

85

86

THE MILES TICKED AWAY QUICKLY NOW.
LATE AFTERNOON THE NEXT DAY, THEY STOPPED
FOR BURGERS ON THE BANKS OF THE MUDDY COLORADO.
A LOCAL COWBOY STEPPED UP TO SAY HELLO.

88

WHEN WOODY DUMAS ARRIVED AT RANCHO NEGRITA INFANTE, THE TEXAS RANGERS WERE STILL SIFTING THROUGH THE DEATH SITE.

FOR WOODY, RITUAL MURDER ALWAYS SEEMED ESPECIALLY GRUESOME AND PERVERSE.

WOODY THOUGHT OF A GUY HE KNEW AS A KID CALLED "THE BUZZARD."

BUZZARD LIVED ON A STEADY DIET OF SHINOLA AND WONDER BREAD.

BUZZARD'S DEAD BODY WAS FOUND IN THE TRASH BIN BEHIND THE PUBLIC LIBRARY.

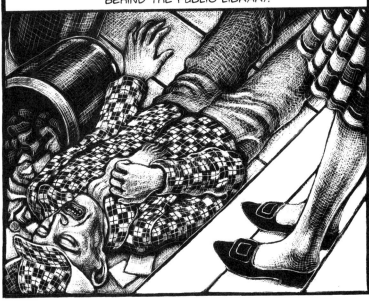

BUZZARD'S ONLY POSSESSION OTHER THAN HIS CLOTHES WAS A MINT CONDITION, 1914 EDITION OF TARZAN OF THE APES.

POOR OLD BUZZARD. GOD I NEED A GOOD STIFF DRINK.

ARRIVING IN L.A., ROMEO DROVE DIRECTLY TO THE HOME OF DOUG AND LILY FAKAOFO IN HACIENDA HEIGHTS, THE SAMOAN-AMERICAN PART OF TOWN.

HEY BUDDY, IT'S BEEN LONG.

TOO LONG, DOUG.

ROMEO AND DOUG HAD BEEN IN THE MARINE CORPS. TOGETHER. ROMEO KNEW HE COULD HIDE DUANE AND ESTELLE WITH THE FAKAOFOS.

DOUG'S WIFE, LILY, WAS VERY UPSET WHEN ROMEO ARRIVED. HER BROTHER, TUTU NUKUONO, HAD JUST BEEN SENT TO FOLSOM PRISON FOR KILLING A COP.

SORRY TO HEAR ABOUT YOUR TROUBLE, LILY.

ACCORDING TO LILY, TUTU'S IMPRISONMENT WAS A BAD JOKE.

TUTU HAD BEEN MINDING HIS OWN BUSINESS DOWN AT THE MIDNIGHT LAGOON WHEN A FIGHT BROKE OUT. INSTINCTIVELY, TUTU TOOK A BASEBALL BAT TO THE FIRST GUY WHO CAME BY WEARING A UNIFORM.

TUTU CAN HANDLE HIMSELF, LILY. COME ON, LET'S GO TO THE MOVIES!

IN WEST HOLLYWOOD, WOODY DUMAS PULLED
INTO THE WILD AT HEART MOTEL, ONE BLOCK WEST
OF SANTOS' WAREHOUSE ON SUNSET BOULEVARD.
WITH TIME TO KILL, WOODY DECIDED TO HANG BY THE POOL.

WOODY NEVER COULD UNDERSTAND WHAT
THE PEOPLE OF LOS ANGELES WERE TALKING ABOUT.

IT WAS AS IF THEY WERE
CONVINCED THAT EVERY-
THING THEY SAID HAD A
DEEPER MEANING.

OH
SHIT!

OR, WAS IT THAT THEY
MEANT SOMETHING MORE
THAN WHAT HE THOUGHT
THEY WERE SAYING?
WOODY JUST DIDN'T GET IT.

95

AT THAT MOMENT, A SAD-FACED MAN SAT DOWN NEXT TO WOODY.

DO YOU MIND IF I SPEAK TO YOU?

NO, GO AHEAD.

I USED TO BE A SINGER. NOT ANY MORE, THOUGH.

WHY'D YOU QUIT?

PEOPLE THOUGHT IT WAS ALCOHOL OR DRUGS. IT WASN'T. I JUST LOST INTEREST IN LIFE.

NO ONE ELSE TO BLAME.

WOULD YOU LIKE HALF MY SANDWICH?

YOU'RE VERY KIND. ARE YOU RELIGIOUS?

NOT PARTICULARLY. HERE, YOU CAN HAVE MY DRINK, TOO. GOODBYE.

96

DOUG AND LILY WENT WITH ROMEO AND PERDITA
TO THE DRIVE-IN. THEY LEFT DUANE AND ESTELLE
TIED UP AND LOCKED IN THE HOUSE.

"... I FEED ON ELECTRICITY, PUNKS ..."

HALF A CONTINENT NOW BEHIND THEM, ROMEO AND PERDITA FINALLY CAME TO REST IN LOS ANGELES.

LILY SAT ALONE IN THE LIVING ROOM.

LILY WAS VERY FRIGHTENED ABOUT DOUG. "ROMEO IS MIXED UP IN VOODOO," SHE THOUGHT. "HE BETTER WATCH HIMSELF WITH THAT STUFF."

THE MAORI PLAYERS WERE BANNED FOR OPENLY URINATING ON THE FIELD AFTER THEIR TEAM SCORED A GOAL.

"THIS IS SIMPLY TRADITION," TRIBAL ELDERS PROTESTED, "MEANT TO GIVE THANKS TO THE GREAT MOTHER AND RESTORE ORDER TO THE WHOLE."

101

LILY'S REVERIE WAS INTERRUPTED BY THE SOUND OF A BULLETIN ON TV.

A GUN BATTLE LEFT TWO DEAD IN THE STREETS OF HOLLYWOOD TONIGHT.

"DEA AGENT WOODROW DUMAS, WHO SET THE TRAP FOR THE TWO DEAD DRUG CARRIERS, SAID THAT THIS WAS AN IMPORTANT CASE."

THIS IS THE FIRST EVIDENCE WE HAVE OF MOB-DIRECTED AFGHAN HEROIN REACHING THE WEST COAST.

"THE DEAD MEN ARE ROMEO DOLOROSA OF KINGSTON, JAMAICA, AND DOUG FAKAOFO, RESIDENT OF HACIENDA HEIGHTS."

"THE HONG KONG TRIADS USED TO CONTROL THIS STUFF, BUT THIS COMES FROM NEW ALLIES. . ."

"THIS IS FROM OUR NEW FRIENDS IN PAKISTAN."

"RELIGIOUS FUNDAMENTALISTS TRAINED BY THE CIA IN EXPLOSIVES, FINANCED BY A MOUNTAIN OF SMACK. . ."

"WE HAVEN'T SEEN THE LAST OF THESE GUYS."

PERDITA DURANGO AND SHORTY DEE WERE SITTING
ON ADJACENT STOOLS AT THE QUICKHIT LOUNGE
INSIDE LOS ANGELES INTERNATIONAL AIRPORT.

106

" . . . IT'S ALWAYS 59 DEGREES AND RAINING IN TUPELO."

110

BRING ME THE HEAD OF
PERDITA DURANGO

An interview with BARRY GIFFORD

Neon Lit: Didn't Perdita Durango start out as a minor character in *Wild At Heart*?

Barry Gifford: Yes, but by the end of that book she had come in, and pretty much began to dominate the scenery. I resisted that, because this was still Sailor and Lula's story and Bobby Peru's story. But upon finishing *Wild at Heart*, I really didn't have much of a choice. I immediately sat down and began to write *Perdita Durango*.

NL: What about the *Wild at Heart* movie?

"You really are dangerously cute, Peanut."
Laura Dern in the David Lynch film adaptation of Barry Gifford's novel, *Wild at Heart*. Dern had already played a key role as the police chief's innocent daughter in Lynch's *Blue Velvet*, before taking on the role of the saucy and endearing Lula Pace Fortune.

How did Isabella Rossellini end up as Perdita Durango in the film David Lynch made of your book?

BG: Isabella wanted the role. There was much attention being paid to the Mexican artist, Frida Kahlo, at the time, remember? Well, Isabella was influenced by Kahlo. She gave herself those Frida Kahlo eyebrows. She gave herself that look, so that she bore a resemblance to Frida Kahlo. And then David decided to throw that blonde wig on her head. I think what Isabella portrayed most in the movie was this image, and she did a great job. It was perfectly in sync with the rest of the film, which became to me

Isabella Rossellini as Perdita Durango in *Wild at Heart*. Another veteran of *Blue Velvet*, Rossellini acted together with Lynch in the 1988 film *Zelly and Me*. The entire text of *Wild at Heart* was filmed by Lynch, including the violent love scene between Perdita Durango and Bobby Peru found in the chapter called "Friends" in the original book. The episode was cut, however, from the final version of the film. "The footage is sitting around in a can somewhere," so Gifford believes.

like this big dark David Lynch musical comedy! I thought it was great. You could hardly consider it boring. But that was David Lynch's *Wild at Heart,* and not necessarily my vision of Perdita Durango. For me Perdita is a survivor, somebody smart and very strong, the kind of character who emerges unscathed, more emotionally developed as the story goes on.

You know, I think one of the things that seems to fascinate a lot of the European critics or the European audiences is the fact that I have very strong women in this series of books. In the Sailor and Lula saga, Lula is the one who matures. Through all of the action, right to the end, Lula is the one who develops, whereas Sailor, being the male, is sort of forced into all this lunkheaded, often criminal behavior. He is really the victim of a patriarchal society.

NL: And Romeo too, like Sailor, is ultimately expendable.

BG: Romeo Dolorosa certainly has an agenda based on a

traditional kind of machismo. But Perdita — she's the machisma. She's really the bright one, and the strong one. And that's really what I try to portray here. You can go back

Faye Dunaway as Bonnie in *Bonnie & Clyde.* This wildly popular 1967 Arthur Penn film was based on the real life escapades of Bonnie Parker and Clyde Barrow. It was as if Romeo and Juliet had found new life in the Dust Bowl. From that point on, hundreds of films based on youth, murder, sex and unemployment would be released internationally each year.

through literary history and point out hundreds of strong women characters, but I don't think there's ever been a character quite like Perdita Durango.

NL: Does Perdita come out of the Mexican tradition, the Mexican cinema?

BG: Not the current Mexican cinema, necessarily. You might get this comic book slapstick like *El Mariachi* that Rodriguez did, but that's absolutely a comic book style. The closest thing it comes from are the movies of Emilio Fernandez in the '40s and '50s in Mexico, where he often had very strong but conflicted and oppressed heroines, which is very, very important.

Mexican actress Isela Vega and Warren Oates in the highly controversial 1974 film by Sam Peckinpah, *Bring Me The Head of Alfredo Garcia*. In its bizarre violence and sense of human degradation, *Perdita Durango* is a humor-filled extension of Peckinpah's cinematic world. In *Perdita Durango*, however, it is as if the meaning of the world will now be articulated not by the invasive gringo, but by one of the native players — one of the women — who have served, historically, only as victims of these attentions in the past.

Dolores del Rio in *In Caliente*. The most beautiful of Hollywood's Mexican actresses, del Rio was born Lolita Dolores Asunsolo de Martinez in Durango in 1905. Her "look" was so engaging that David Selznick was alleged to have said: "I don't care what story you use so long as we call it *Bird of Paradise,* and del Rio jumps into a flaming volcano at the finish."

eckinpah figures in here. Peckinpah is a student of Fernandez. The haracter played by Isela Vega, for example, in *Bring Me The Head Of Alfredo Garcia,* that's the kind of character that Perdita Durango is. A rostitute, yet somebody who is also very much her own person, some-ne who has managed to survive somehow in this excruciatingly

NL: We were wondering . . . have we seen the last of Perdita? In a later novel, *Sultans of Africa*, you have her married off to this minor gangster, Poppy Papavero, but it's easy to see our Perdita growing bored with middle-class married life real fast.

BG: Well, you know, her husband is in fact killed — Poppy Papavero is killed in that book. There is certainly a real possibility that I'm not finished with Perdita.

NL: So what's going on with the film of *Perdita Durango*?

BG: The latest is that a young Spanish director named Alex De La Iglesia is going to be directing the film. Victoria Abril, the star of many of Pedro Almodóvar movies, is playing Perdita.

NL: Has a time line been set?

BG: Well it's supposed to start in September, 1995 — that's what the trades say.

NL: Will it be shot in the U.S.?

BG: It was going to be shot around Tucson. I wrote the first draft of the screenplay and the rewrite is being done by David Trueba, Fernando Trueba's brother. Fernando Trueba directed *Belle Epoque*. That's really all I know. And as far as I know it's supposed to be in English, an American film.

NL: With a largely Spanish cast?

BG: We'll see. You and I will buy the tickets when it comes out.

NL: And so the adventures go on. Particularly as we cross the border into the Hispanic worlds, how far are we, really, from that ultimate Spanish road novel, *Don Quixote*? It seems to me if people miss the humor — the pitch-black satire in your work — those windmills, they miss the essence of the work.

BG: Right. I am primarily a satirist. A dark satirist. The funny thing was when I was being interviewed a lot for *Wild at Heart*, some of the critics kept saying "Now here is a road novel in the tradition of Jack Kerouac's *On the Road*," and of course Larry Lee and I had done a biography of Kerouac, and later Francis Ford Coppola would ask me to write the screenplay for *On the Road*. But, even at the time, I was

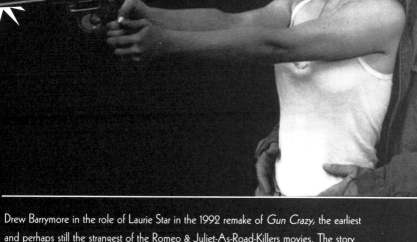

Drew Barrymore in the role of Laurie Star in the 1992 remake of *Gun Crazy*, the earliest and perhaps still the strangest of the Romeo & Juliet-As-Road-Killers movies. The story was first written by MacKinlay Kantor for the Saturday Evening Post, and then released as a movie by director Joseph E. Lewis under the title *Deadly Is The Female*. It was called back, however, seven months later, and re-released under its current, popular title.

Tura Satana in Russ Meyer's 1966 *Faster Pussycat, Kill! Kill!* The Native American-born Satana's performance had a lasting impact on Gifford. "No Tura Satana," the author has said, "no Perdita Durango."

saying, hell, wait a minute, this goes back a whole lot further than Kerouac. What about Cervantes?

You know twice now I have had this conversation with Pedro Almodóvar, because Pedro is from La Mancha, and Pedro was approached to do a film of *Don Quixote*. Pedro doesn't want to do Quixote, but he does love Perdita. One of his favorite actresses will be playing Perdita in the movie. There are enough new windmills around to do battle with inside the world of Perdita Durango.

WILLIAM LINDSAY GRESHAM'S
NIGHTMARE ALLEY

William Lindsay Gresham's *Nightmare Alley* is one of the most fascinating carnival novels ever written. Gresham's side-show portraits of Bruno Hertz, the half-African ape, half-Greek god strongman; Major Mosquito, the tiniest human being on record; Sailor "Tattoo" Martin, the human portrait gallery; Mamzelle Electra, the girl in the electric chair; and the ever-present, always nameless Geek remain among the most compelling and bizarre character galleries ever to be found inside the pages of a contemporary novel.

Produced by Georgie Jessel, with expressionistic, low-key photography by the talented Lee Garmes, and featuring a number one song — "The Theme from Nightmare Alley" — by the then-young jazz pianist, Nat "King" Cole — a film of *Nightmare Alley* was made in 1948. In the film, Tyrone Power played the role of spiritualist and con-man, Stan Carlisle. The role of the erotic Madam Zeena — miracle woman of the age — was played by the wonderful Joan Blondell.

The movie version of this classic novel went south, however, almost upon release. These days it can be found, if at all, at three o'clock in the morning, in the middle of some independent television market lost in the wilds of North Dakota.

The genius of the original story, however, and the truly odd touches employed by the author, make this book a challenging rescue operation for Neon Lit. Scheduled for release in the fall of 1996, featuring the art of Spain Rodriguez, with a script by Spain, Bob Callahan and Tom De Haven, the first Neon Lit edition of William Lindsay Gresham's *Nightmare Alley* will be published as the third volume in this ongoing library of exceptional illustrated postmodern crime fiction.